Lincoln Peirce

BiG NATE

WHAT COULD POSSIBLY GO WRONG?

HarperCollins *Children's Books*

HarperCollins *Children's Books* is a division of HarperCollins*Publishers* Ltd,
77-85 Fulham Palace Road, Hammersmith, London, W6 8JB.

These comic strips first appeared in newspapers between
5th November 2007 and 8th June 2008.

The HarperCollins website address is: www.harpercollins.co.uk

1

Text and illustration copyright © 2012 United Feature Syndicate, Inc.

ISBN 978-0-00-747831-6

The author asserts the moral right to be identified as the author of the work.

Printed and bound in England by
Clays Ltd, St Ives plc

MIX
Paper from
responsible sources
FSC
www.fsc.org   FSC C007454

FSC™ is a non-profit international organisation established to promote
the responsible management of the world's forests. Products carrying the
FSC label are independently certified to assure consumers that they come
from forests that are managed to meet the social, economic and
ecological needs of present and future generations,
and other controlled sources.

Find out more about HarperCollins and the environment at
www.harpercollins.co.uk/green

MRS GODFREY
TO THE RESCUE

© 2007 by NEA, Inc.

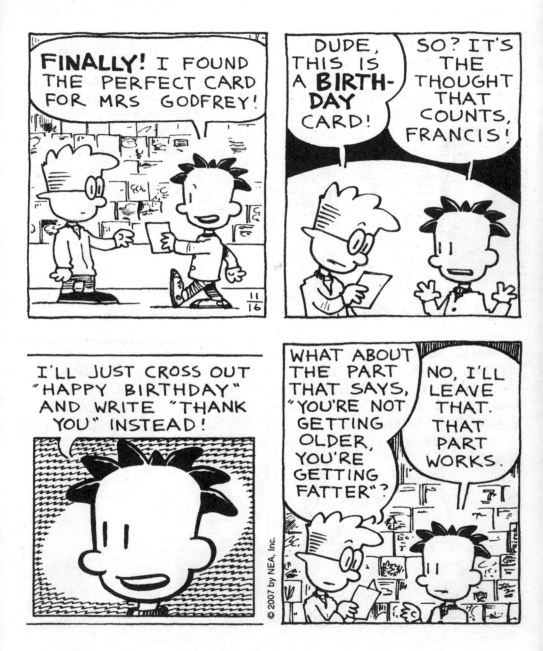

WHO WANTS TO PLAY
SOCIAL STUDIES JEOPARDY?

18

YOU KEEP ASKING IF WE CAN DO SOMETHING FUN IN CLASS, NATE. WELL, TODAY WE'RE PLAYING "SOCIAL STUDIES JEOPARDY".

REALLY?

OUR CATEGORIES ARE "THE SPIRIT OF '76", "STATE CAPITALS", "THE BILL OF RIGHTS", "THE BOSTON TEA PARTY"...

UH... HOLD IT, HOLD IT!

ALL THOSE CATEGORIES ARE, LIKE, **SOCIAL STUDIES** STUFF!

...WHICH IS WHY IT'S CALLED "SOCIAL STUDIES JEOPARDY", PINHEAD.

NO "TV SITCOMS"? NO "POTENT POTABLES"?

11/24

Peirce

THE STATE MOTTO OF MASSA-CHUSETTS, CHAD?
WHAT IS "THE BAY STATE"?
BING!
NO. NATE?
UH... WHAT IS "OLD COLONY"?
BING!
11 28
NO. GINA?
WHAT IS "ENSE PETIT PLACIDAM SUB LIBERTATE QUIETEM"?
BING!
© 2007 by NEA, Inc.
VERY GOOD, GINA!
YOU'RE SICK.

CHAMPS, OR NOT?

DOGS VS. CATS

'TIS THE SEASON

57

THE BOOK OF FACTS = BOR-ING!

HOW'S FRANCIS DOING WITHOUT HIS BOOK OF FACTS?

NOT GOOD.

DID YOU KNOW THAT THE CAPITAL OF DJIBOUTI IS ROSEAU? WAIT!... NO, THAT CAN'T BE RIGHT... UH... THE CAPITAL OF ROSEAU IS...

UH... HOLD IT, LET ME START OVER!... DID YOU KNOW THAT THE COMPOSER ARTURO "HOT LIPS" O'FARRILL WAS... UM... NO, WAIT, HIS NICKNAME WASN'T "HOT LIPS", IT WAS... DANG, WHAT **WAS** IT?...

1/10

OKAY, LET'S TALK ABOUT RAILROADS! THE NUMBER OF TOTAL MILES OF TRACK IN 1930 WAS OVER BRITNEY S WHEN A IN NO, THAT DOESN'T MAKE SENSE! I'LL HAVE TO G

HE'S TRYING TO FREE-STYLE.

THIS IS UGLY.

RELAX...OR ELSE!

ART À LA NATE

RRRINNNG!

1/27

HOO!
HOO! GASP!
PUFF!

© 2008 by NEA, Inc.

WRIGHT

BEAT YOU TO IT.

WRIGHT

I HATE REPORT CARD DAY.

WHO GETS AN "UNSATISFACTORY" IN STUDY HALL?

WHO'S THE PERFECT COUPLE?

NATE WRIGHT, FOOD CRITIC

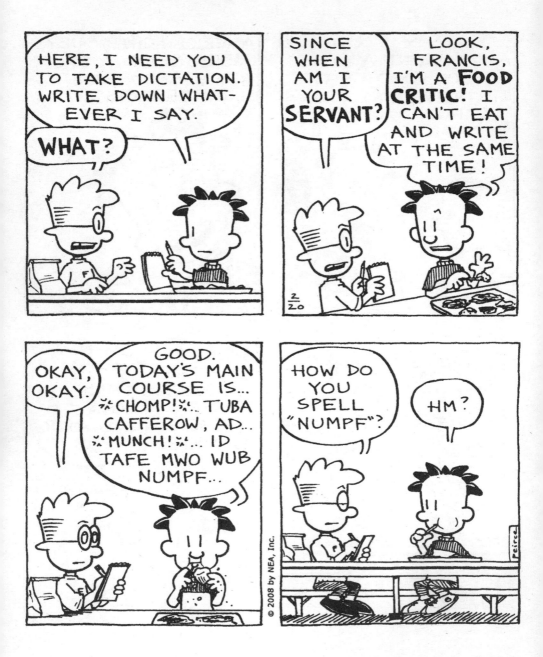

At 11:35 yesterday morning, as I sat in the cafeteria looking down at the "lunch" before me, I immediately regretted my decision to become the school food critic.

The so-called "fish sticks" looked and tasted like a block of moist sawdust. The garden salad was reminiscent of a sickly chia pet. And the ice-cold Tater Tots appeared to have been cooked under a 60-watt light bulb.

$\frac{2}{22}$

Of the bread pudding I will say only two words: gag reflex. I spent most of the afternoon getting violently ill in the second-floor bathroom. TOMORROW: MEAT LOAF CONFIDENTIAL!

IN THE FOOD CRITIC BIZ, THAT'S WHAT IS KNOWN AS "DISHING IT OUT".

WHAT'S WITH BODY LANGUAGE?

RUBBER BANDS RULE!

ARE YOU
COOL ENOUGH?

THE PERFECT DATE

DETENTION, AGAIN

BOOK BUDDIES, NATE'S WAY

ARE YOU FEELING ALL RIGHT, PETER? YOU LOOK A LITTLE PALE.

ME? I'M FINE.

IN FACT, I'M **MORE** THAN FINE! I'M HEALTHY ASH A HORSHE! I'VE NEVER FELT BETTER IN MY **LIFE!**

OH, GOOD. I WOULDN'T WANT YOU TO MISS BOOK BUDDY TIME!

B-BOOK BUDDY TIME?

PETER, M'LAD!

ACTUALLY, I'M SHTARTING TO GET A SHPLITTING HEADACHE.

ALL RIGHT, EVERYONE, I'M AFRAID BOOK BUDDY TIME IS OVER!

AWWWW!

NATE, HOW'D IT GO WITH PETER?

IT WAS AWESOME!

HE'S TOO SMART TO NEED HELP WITH HIS READING, SO INSTEAD I TAUGHT HIM HOW TO PLAY TEXAS HOLD 'EM!

ANTE UP, PEOPLESH! LET'SH SHEE THAT LUNCH MONEY!

MY WORK HERE IS DONE.

CRUSHED

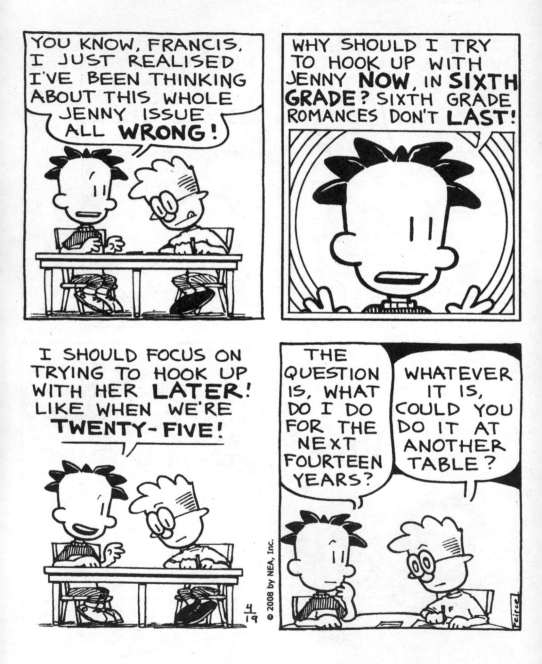

SECRET FAN

BATTER UP!

WHAT COULD POSSIBLY GO WRONG?

MRS GODFREY'S GOING TO LUNCH! HER ROOM'S EMPTY!
5/13
I'M GOIN' IN.
GOOD LUCK.
I'D TELL YOU NOT TO DO ANY-THING STUPID, BUT IT'S A LITTLE LATE FOR THAT.
© 2008 by NEA, Inc.
SPEAKING OF DOING STUPID THINGS, ASKING FRANCIS TO BE MY LOOKOUT WAS A BONEHEAD MOVE.
Peirce

5/15

THE LIST

203

BRAINIAC

ROCKIN' OUT

STUCK ON NATE

BONUS ACTIVITIES TO CRACK YOU UP!

ALL MIXED UP

Can you match each of Nate's sketches to the correct strip?

SUPERCOOL CAPTIONS

Can you come up with captions for Nate's sketches?

SUPER CHALLENGE: Guess which sketch goes with the Sunday comic strips on pages 49, 59, 112, 151:

Comic A goes on page _____.

Comic B goes on page _____.

Comic C goes on page _____.

Comic D goes on page _____.

NATE ≠ NEAT

Have you ever scrambled the letters in your name to see if they spell anything else? Well, **I** have. And guess what: **MY** letters spell **N·E·A·T!**

KSSSCH!

Pretty ironic, right? Hey, I realise I'm not exactly Joe Tidy. **EVERYBODY** knows it. But that doesn't stop Francis, who color-codes his underwear, from pointing it out about a jillion times a day.

Your desk is **DISGUSTING**. You have pai__ on your shirt. Oh, and you h__ __heez Doodl__ __tains __ __er y__ __ace. What __ __OB yo__ __re!

Francis has been telling me to clean up my act since I poured applesauce down his pants back in kindergarten. Of course, I've always ignored him. But then last week my sloppiness got Francis in trouble... and he **NEVER** gets in trouble!

I felt so bad about it, I decided to actually try to get neater. And thanks to

I'm **VERY** disappointed in you.

Oops.

Teddy and his uncle Pedro, the hypnotist, it's working... **TOO** well. All of the sudden, I'm starting to act **JUST LIKE FRANCIS!** Frankly, I think I'm losing my mind.

You're doing **GREAT!**

I'm **FLIPPIN' OUT!**

What a **MESS!**
Read all about it in
BIG NATE FLIPS OUT!!

NATE RATES ALL THE Big NATE BOOKS!

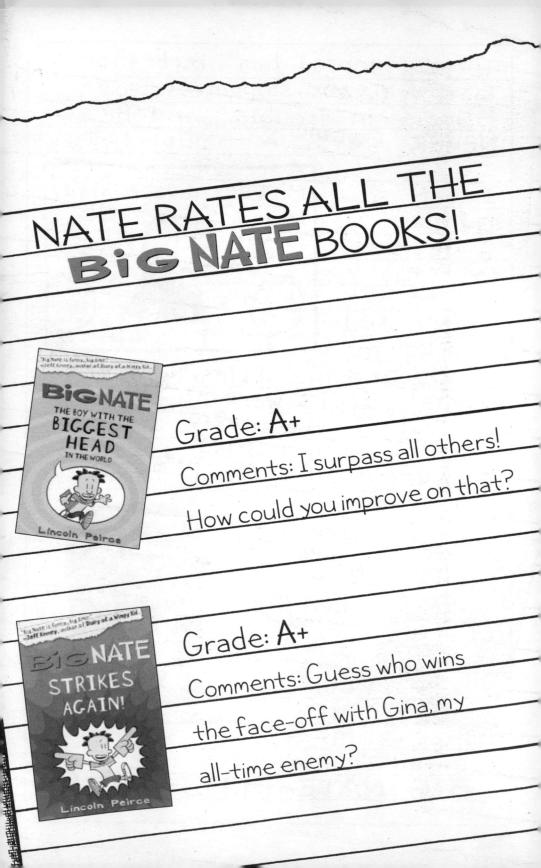

Grade: **A+**

Comments: I surpass all others!

How could you improve on that?

Grade: **A+**

Comments: Guess who wins

the face-off with Gina, my

all-time enemy?

Grade: A+

Comments: Guaranteed to beat boredom, and definitely NOT boring!

Grade: A+

Comments: Nate—hero

Artur—zero

Because I'm on a roll!

Grade: A+

Comments: Even when life's not awesome, I am!

The only time I've gotten straight As! That's why YOU need all the books!

Lincoln Peirce

(pronounced "purse") is a cartoonist/writer and *New York Times* bestselling author of the hilarious Big Nate book series (www.bignatebooks.com), now published in twenty-two countries worldwide. He is also the creator of the comic strip *Big Nate*, which appears in over two hundred and fifty U.S. newspapers and online daily at www.bignate.com. Lincoln's boyhood idol was Charles Schulz of *Peanuts* fame, but his main inspiration for Big Nate has always been his own experience as a sixth grader. Just like Nate, Lincoln loves comics, ice hockey, and Cheez Doodles (and dislikes cats, figure skating, and egg salad). His Big Nate books have been featured on *Good Morning America* and in *USA Today*, the *Washington Post*, and the *Boston Globe*. He has also written for Cartoon Network and Nickelodeon. Lincoln lives with his wife and two children in Portland, Maine.